'13.65

First Day of School

ALL ABOUT SHAPES AND SIZES

Written by Kirsten Hall

Illustrated by Bev Luedecke

children's press®

A Division of Scholastic Inc.
New York Toronto London Auckland Sydney
Mexico City New Delhi Hong Kong
Danbury, Connecticut

About the Author

Kirsten Hall, formerly an early-childhood teacher, is a children's book editor in New York City. She has been writing books for children since she was thirteen years old and now has over sixty titles in print.

About the Illustrator

Bev Luedecke enjoys life and nature in Colorado. Her sparkling personality and artistic flair are reflected in her creation of Beastieville, a world filled with lovable Beasties that are sure to delight children of all ages.

Library of Congress Cataloging-in-Publication Data

Hall, Kirsten.
 First day of school : all about shapes and sizes / written by Kirsten Hall ; illustrated by Bev Luedecke.
    p. cm.
Summary: When the Beasties arrive in Mr. Rigby's classroom on the first day of school, the "one size fits all" seats will not fit.
 ISBN 0-516-22893-5 (lib. bdg.)   0-516-24654-2 (pbk.)
 [1. Teachers–Fiction. 2. First day of school–Fiction. 3. Schools–Fiction. 4. Individuality–Fiction. 5. Stories in rhyme.] I. Luedecke, Bev, ill. II. Title.
 PZ8.3.H146Fi 2003
 [E]–dc21
                            2003001589

1 2 3 4 5 6 7 8 9 10 R 12 11 10 09 08 07 06 05 04 03

A NOTE TO PARENTS AND TEACHERS

Welcome to the world of the Beasties, where learning is FUN. In each of the charming stories in this series, the Beasties deal with character traits that every child can identify with. Each story reinforces appropriate concept skills for kinder-gartners and first graders, while simultaneously encouraging problem-solving skills. Following are just a few of the ways that you can help children get the most from this delightful series.

Stories to be read and enjoyed

Encourage children to read the stories aloud. The rhyming verses make them fun to read. Then ask them to think about alternate solutions to some of the prob-lems that the Beasties have faced or to imagine alternative endings. Invite chil-dren to think about what they would have done if they were in the story and to recall similar things that have happened to them.

Activities reinforce the learning experience

The activities at the end of the books offer a way for children to put their new skills to work. They complement the story and are designed to help children develop specific skills and build confidence. Use these activities to reinforce skills. But don't stop there. Encourage children to find ways to build on these skills during the course of the day.

Learning opportunities are everywhere

Use this book as a starting point for talking about how we use reading skills or math or social studies concepts in everyday life. When we search for a phone number in the telephone book and scan names in alphabetical order or check a list, we are using reading skills. When we keep score at a baseball game or divide a class into even-numbered teams, we are using math.

The more you can help children see that the skills they are learning in school really do have a place in everyday life, the more they will think of learning as something that is part of their lives, not as a chore to be borne. Plus you will be sending the important message that learning is fun.

Madeline Boskey Olsen, Ph.D.
Developmental Psychologist

Bee-Bop

Puddles

Slider

Wilbur

Pip & Zip

Flippet

Pooky

Mr. Rigby

Smudge

We're
the
Beasties

Toggles

Mr. Rigby is a teacher.
He has many things to do.
Tomorrow he will meet his students.
Everything must look like new.

He lines the desks and chairs up neatly.
He puts a big map on the wall.
He hangs a plant. He cleans the board.
He hopes his students love it all!

It is Monday. "Hello class!
Each of you can have a treat!"

The day is starting off so nicely.
Now it is time to take a seat.

Uh-oh! Pip is having problems.
She keeps rolling off her chair!

Zip is rolling off his chair, too.
Everyone has stopped to stare.

Slider has another problem.
His chair should be thin and long.

Flippet does not like her new chair.
It is dry. That just feels wrong!

Puddles does not like her new seat.
She does not know where to spray.

Bee-Bop has a problem, too.
Great big Smudge is in the way!

Wilbur does not like his new seat.
Why must he sit in the back?

Smudge is much too big for his chair.
Oops! He thinks that was a crack!

What will Mr. Rigby do now?
Where will all his students sit?

Everything is such a mess.
It looks just like a storm has hit!

The day is over. School is out.
Mr. Rigby shakes each hand.
He looks around his classroom.
There is not even room to stand!

He waves good-bye to his new students.
He looks around and says, "Oh, dear!"

Pooky stops and taps his teacher.
He speaks softly in his ear.

When the class comes back on Tuesday,
They do not know what to think.

Mr. Rigby looks at Pooky.
Pooky gives a little wink.

Everyone is very happy!
Mr. Rigby saved the day.
The students thank him for his hard work.
Mr. Rigby gets an A!

29

CLASS COUNT

1. How many desks does Mr. Rigby set up?

2. How many posters are on the classroom walls?

3. How many pencils does Mr. Rigby have on top of his desk?

4. How many letters are written on the board?

SOUNDS LIKE...

The word "scare" sounds a lot like "chair". Can you think of other words that sound like "scare"?

LET'S TALK ABOUT IT

The first day of school comes around once a year.

1. How do you feel when it's time to go back to school?

2. What do you like most about your classroom?

3. What do you like most about your teacher?

4. What kinds of things do you like to learn about?

WORD LIST

a	feels	look	rolling	they
all	Flippet	looks	room	thin
an	for	love	saved	things
and	gets	many	says	think
another	gives	map	school	thinks
around	good-bye	meet	seat	time
at	great	mess	shakes	to
back	hand	Monday	she	tomorrow
be	hangs	Mr.	should	too
Bee-Bop	happy	much	sit	treat
big	hard	must	Slider	Tuesday
board	has	neatly	Smudge	uh-oh
can	have	new	so	up
chair	having	nicely	softly	very
chairs	he	not	speaks	wall
class	hello	now	spray	was
classroom	her	of	stand	waves
cleans	him	off	stare	way
comes	his	oh	starting	what
crack	hit	on	stopped	when
day	hopes	oops	stops	where
dear	in	out	storm	why
desks	is	over	students	Wilbur
do	it	Pip	such	will
does	just	plant	take	wink
dry	keeps	Pooky	taps	work
each	know	problem	teacher	wrong
ear	like	problems	thank	you
even	lines	Puddles	that	Zip
everyone	little	puts	the	
everything	long	Rigby	there	